SP⚬T

the DIFFERENCE

PAPP Puzzles™

Visit our website to find
more quality products:
www.pappinternational.com

Art Director: Tammy Desnoyers
Design: Rafaela Petel Ruiz
Images: © Shutterstock

PAPP International Inc.
3700 Griffith Street, Suite 395,
Montreal (Quebec), Canada H4T 2B3

ONE
TREE
PLANTED

A portion of the proceeds from the sale of this book
goes toward reforestation and the Million Tree Challenge.

www.onetreeplanted.org

PUZZLE 3

FIND THE 10 CHANGES & KEEP SCORE

ANSWERS ON PAGE 30

PUZZLE 4

ONE OF THESE IS NOT LIKE THE OTHERS, CAN YOU SPOT THE DIFFERENCE ?

ANSWER ON PAGE 30

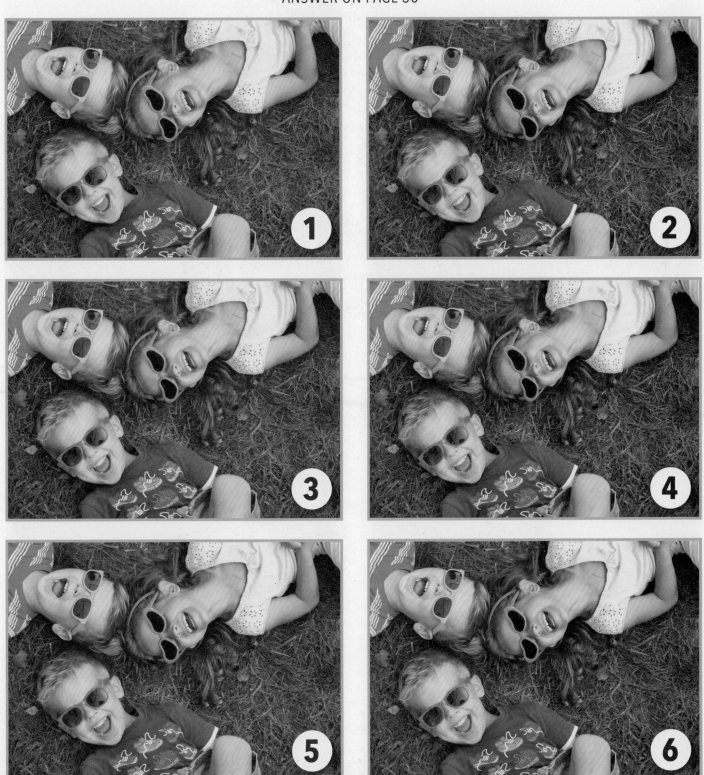

PUZZLE 8

FIND THE 6 CHANGES & KEEP SCORE

☐ ☐ ☐ ☐ ☐ ☐

ANSWERS ON PAGE 31

PUZZLE 9

ONE OF THESE IS NOT LIKE THE OTHERS,
CAN YOU SPOT THE DIFFERENCE?

ANSWER ON PAGE 31

PUZZLE 13

FIND THE 12 CHANGES & KEEP SCORE

☐ ☐ ☐ ☐ ☐ ☐ ☐ ☐ ☐ ☐ ☐ ☐

ANSWERS ON PAGE 32

PUZZLE 14

ONE OF THESE IS NOT LIKE THE OTHERS, CAN YOU SPOT THE DIFFERENCE?

ANSWER ON PAGE 32

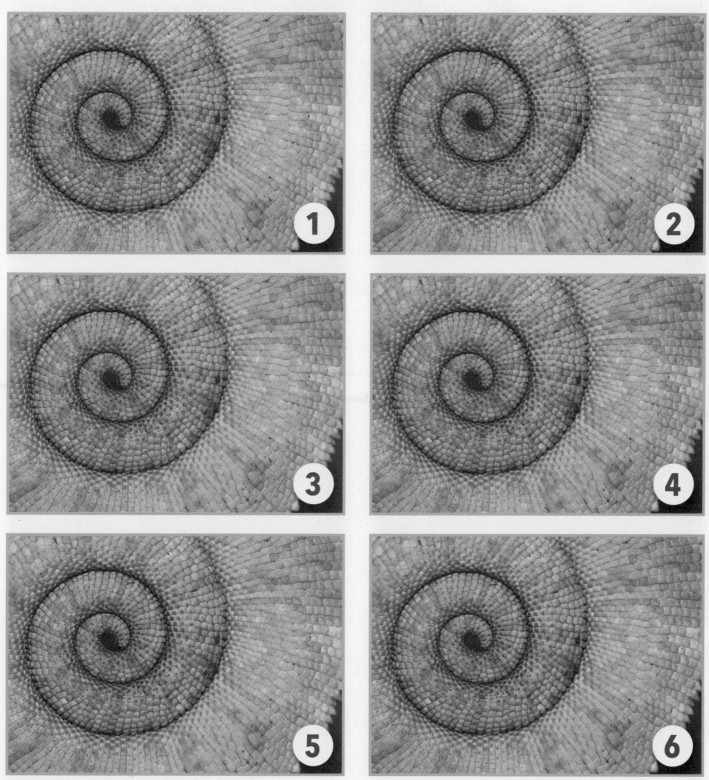

ANSWERS

PUZZLE 1 | **Page 3**

PUZZLE 2 | **Page 5**

PUZZLE 3 | **Page 6**

PUZZLE 4 | **Page 7**

PUZZLE 5 | **Page 9**

PUZZLE 6 | **Page 11**

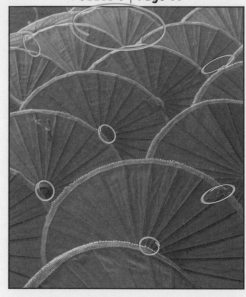

PUZZLE 7 | **Page 13**

PUZZLE 8 | **Page 14**

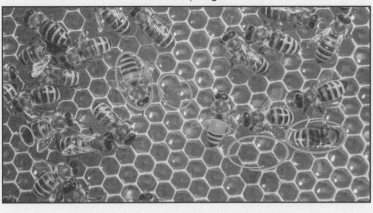

PUZZLE 9 | **Page 15**

PUZZLE 10 | **Page 17**

PUZZLE 11 | **Page 19**

PUZZLE 12 | **Page 21**

SPOT THE DIFFERENCE ANSWERS • 31

PUZZLE 13 | **Page 22**

PUZZLE 14 | **Page 23**

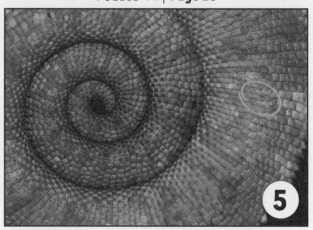

PUZZLE 15 | **Page 25**

PUZZLE 16 | **Page 27**

PUZZLE 17 | **Page 29**